The activities

- The activities in this book are designed to show whether your children are 'ready' to read or are ready for a more difficult reading level. Their wish to read is the best sign of readiness.

- Many skills are involved, but most of them will be mastered unconsciously, just as your children learned to talk without direct teaching. They do not have to be equally good at, for instance, seeing letters distinctly, drawing, copying or telling a story. Success in particular activities should help you to find their strong points.

- The chart on page 32 details some of the skills and the ways these are linked with progress in learning to read.

The stories at Level 5

- The plots of the stories at this level are more complicated, and children should enjoy guessing 'what might come next' or 'what the ending will be'. Encourage this feeling of anticipation and involvement in the text, which helps maintain your child's interest. Remember, no child will like the same stories equally; it is worthwhile discussing with your children why they prefer some stories to others.

- Your child may be ready to initiate the reading now, by reading through the story alone on the first read. Don't worry if this doesn't happen. It is still important that you go on sharing the stories together. Continue the practice of 'reading together' as before. Suggest that your children join in with the reading and when they are ready, they

toge...

Take it in turns for ...... ad the narrative, and the other to read the characters' speeches. (It would be best on the first read through for you to take the narrative.) If a word is causing a problem, supply it, so that the flow of the story is kept going. Mistakes will be made, but this is a good sign, because it shows that your child is willing to try. Above all don't stop the reading in mid-stream to correct any mistakes. Wait until the end of a page or so, and then say "Let's look at that bit again" and read it yourself, perhaps pointing out the words that were mistaken.

- Besides reading the whole story to you, your child will now want to read it to another audience — a brother or sister, a pet, a doll or a teddy.

- Don't rush quickly onto another book. Remind your child of the stories that have already been read in the earlier levels. Bring in incidents from the stories into your ordinary conversation; for example, compare your breakfast with that of Robby Robot!

- If you have a tape-recorder, you might like to record your reading together. Let your child read alternate pages with you. Listen to the playback together; this helps to emphasise the way that the voice makes the reading more 'interesting'.

The activities at Level 5

- Most of the activities at this level are intended for your child to attempt alone, although help may still be needed with the instructions. Be sure to read through all the activities yourself first — some may involve you as an audience. Emphasise the 'fun' aspect of the activities, and at all costs avoid the impression that they are 'tests'.

- There is no need for your child to work through the activities in sequence. If your child glances through to select which activity is the favourite one for today, this will help with the development of the important skills of skimming and scanning (quickly selecting the information you need) when reading material.

- Your children might like to build up a 'Book of things I have done from my stories'. This would give a sense of achievement and permanence, as well as enabling you to keep a check on their development and what has been done.

- When all the activities have been done, encourage your child to read the story again before you move on to another book.

2

Horses of
the Sun God

by Helen Arnold

Illustrated by Thomas Atkinson
and Tony Kenyon

A Piccolo Original
In association with Macmillan Education

Liz is reading a book.

It's a book about the Sun God.

The Sun God rides across the sky.

Each day he rises in the East.

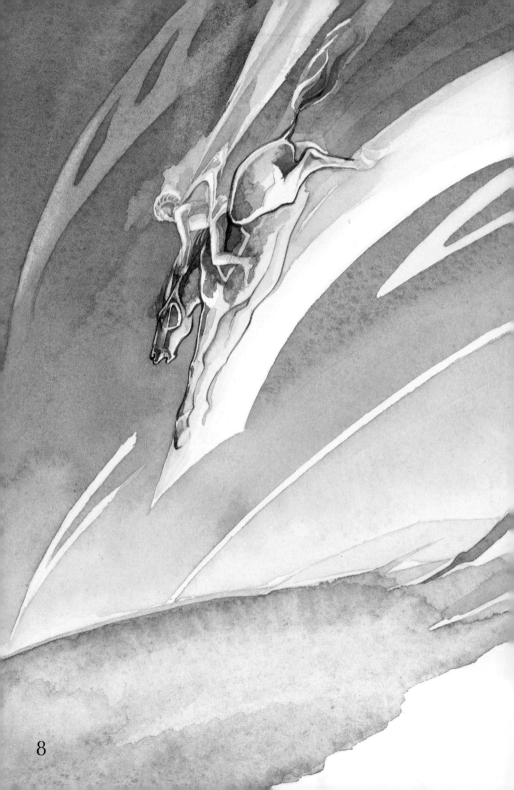

He rides across the sky to the West.
He carries the golden disc of the sun.   9

10   The Sun God has five beautiful horses.

One horse is of turquoise.

11

One horse is of white shell.

One horse is of pearl shell.

One horse is of red shell.

One horse is of black coal.

When the skies are blue and
the weather is fine, the Sun God
rides his turquoise horse,

or his horse of white shell,

or his horse of pearl shell.

When the skies are dark with storm clouds, the Sun God rides his red horse,

or his horse of black coal.

23

Each day he rises in the East.

He rides across the sky to the West.

25

He rides on one of his five horses and
carries the golden disc of the sun.

Things to talk about

1. Look at this picture of a compass. Can you see the letters **N**
   S E and **W** on it? These letters stand for North, South, East
   and West which are the four main points on a compass. A
   compass helps people find out the direction in which they
   are travelling.

   Look at the pictures in the story.
   In which direction does the Sun God travel?

   Where does the sun rise where we live?
   Where does it set?

Looking at pictures and words

2. Can you remember the colours of the horses of
the Sun God?
Which colour do you like best?
Can you think of any other colours?

1. Can you find the picture in the story which matches each of these sentences?

Each day he rises in the East.

One horse is of pearl shell.

The Sun God has five beautiful horses.

One horse is of black coal.

2. Some of these sentences are in the story, but some are not. Which ones are not in the story?

The Sun God has five horses.

The Sun God rises in the South.

When the skies are dark, the Sun God rides his black horse.

The Sun God has a grey horse.

The Sun God rides across the land.

The Sun God carries the silver disc of the moon.

Things to do

1. Draw one of the Sun God's horses and colour it. Can you write the colour of the horse underneath?

2. Do you know what the colours of the rainbow are? Can you draw a rainbow and write down all the different colours in it?

These activities and skills:	will help your children to:
Looking and remembering	hold a story in their heads, retell it in their own words.
Listening, being able to tell the difference between sounds	remember sounds in words and link spoken words with the words they see in print.
Naming things and using different words to explain or retell events	recognise different words in print, build their vocabulary and guess at the meaning of words.
Matching, seeing patterns, similarities and differences	recognise letters, see patterns within words, use the patterns to read 'new' words and split long words into syllables.
Knowing the grammatical patterns of spoken language	guess the word-order in reading.
Anticipating what is likely to happen next in a story	guess what the next sentence or event is likely to be about.
Colouring, getting control of pencils and pens, copying and spelling	produce their own writing, which will help them to understand the way English is written.
Understanding new experiences by linking them to what they already know	read with understanding and think about what they have read.
Understanding their own feelings and those of others	enjoy and respond to stories and identify with the characters.

First published 1990 by Pan Books Ltd, Cavaye Place, London SW10 9PG

9 8 7 6 5 4 3 2 1

Editorial consultant: Donna Bailey

© Pan Books Ltd and Macmillan Publishers Ltd 1990. Text © Helen Arnold 1990

British Library Cataloguing in Publication Data
Arnold, Helen
Horses of the Sun God.
1. English language. Readers — For children
I. Title II. Series
428.6
ISBN 0–330–30701–0

Printed in Hong Kong